PECULIAR PETS

2021

Amazing Creatures

Edited By Debbie Killingworth

First published in Great Britain in 2021 by:

 Young**Writers**® Est. 1991

Young Writers
Remus House
Coltsfoot Drive
Peterborough
PE2 9BF
Telephone: 01733 890066
Website: www.youngwriters.co.uk

All Rights Reserved
Book Design by Ashley Janson
© Copyright Contributors 2021
Softback ISBN 978-1-80015-483-4

Printed and bound in the UK by BookPrintingUK
Website: www.bookprintinguk.com
YB0475H

★ FOREWORD ★

Welcome Reader!

Are you ready to discover weird and wonderful creatures that you'd never even dreamed of?

For Young Writers' latest competition we asked primary school pupils to create a Peculiar Pet of their own invention, and then write a poem about it! They rose to the challenge magnificently and the result is this fantastic collection full of creepy critters and amazing animals!

Here at Young Writers our aim is to encourage creativity in children and to inspire a love of the written word, so it's great to get such an amazing response, with some absolutely fantastic poems. Not only have these young authors created imaginative and inventive animals, they've also crafted wonderful poems to showcase their creations and their writing ability. These poems are brimming with inspiration. The slimiest slitherers, the creepiest crawlers and furriest friends are all brought to life in these pages – you can decide for yourself which ones you'd like as a pet!

I'd like to congratulate all the young authors in this anthology, I hope this inspires them to continue with their creative writing.

★

★ CONTENTS ★

Perri Haste (7) — 62
Robert Chipernea (10) — 63

Kingsdown School, Southend-On-Sea

Harry Murphy — 64
Toby Ward (14) — 65
Sam Kempen (14) — 66
Eddie Lewis — 67
James Beaumont — 68

St Joseph's Catholic Primary School, Deptford

Great Celestine (9) — 69
Caitlyn Torsu (9) — 70
Michal Kamau (10) — 72
Jordan Okeke (10) — 73
David Okebu (10) — 74
Leslie Salinas Laserna (10) — 75
Caleb Luyimbazi (10) — 76
Selina Sarpong (10) — 77
Manasse Mfutila (9) — 78
Hephzibah Akinbosoye (10) — 79

The Village Prep School, Belsize Park

Jessica Miro (7) — 80
Iman Farid (7) — 81
Victoria Mantzouki (8) — 82
Alina Alexeeva (9) — 83
Arabella McGregor (10) — 84

Weavervale Primary School, Frodsham

Daisy Wilson (8) — 85
Sofia Clare (9) — 86
Melissa Winter (8) — 87
Gracie Garner (8) — 88
Jamie O'Grady — 89
Luke McCabe-Boutrus (9) — 90
Thomas Fairfield (8) — 91

White Court School, Great Notley

Iqra Chaudhry (10) — 92
Austeja Andrulyte (10) — 94
Samuel Weeks (10) — 96
Emily Oliver (9) — 98
Lauren Elizabeth Sibley (9) — 100
Jack Clow (9) — 101
James Smith (10) — 102
Emily Coe (10) — 103
Abigail Hodgson (10) — 104
Matthew McGlone (10) — 105
Lauren J (10) — 106
Gracie Card (9) — 108
Dexter Michael Bernardo (10) — 109
Poppy Chambers (10) — 110
Imogen Louise Sibley (9) — 111
Ethan Gold (10) — 112
Oliver Reid (10) — 113
Louie Knott (10) — 114
Isabel Gladen (9) — 116
Amelia Coulson (10) — 117
Jemima Knighton (10) — 118
Dominic Baktai (10) — 119
Lucas Simpson (10) — 120
Alfie Reeve (10) — 121
Khloe Williamson (10) — 122
Lia Dicker (9) — 123
Ellie-Rose Porter (10) — 124
Alex Levine (10) — 125
Aimee Baker (10) — 126
Sophia Tillbrook (10) — 127
Olivia Blackaby (10) — 128
Taylor Johnson (9) — 129
Harry Cross (9) — 130
Franklyn Limber (9) — 131
Thomas James (9) — 132
Charlie Sellers (9) — 133
Amelia Bullus (10) — 134
Orla Martin (10) — 135
Finn Lawford (10) — 136
Gabriella Lane (9) — 137
Ashley Taylor (9) — 138
Daniel James Walker (9) — 139

Archie Murphy (9)	140
Isla Mooney (10)	141
Harrison Aldred (10)	142
Carson Oram (10)	143
Kolby Bronze (10)	144
Alfie Joyce (9)	145
Harriet Snow (10)	146
Lily-Mai Bull (10)	147
Alfie Eley (10)	148
Nevaeh Matheou (10)	149
James Bullus (10)	150
Eshaan Patel (10)	151
Noah Murphy (10)	152
Yhana Kuta (10)	153

THE POEMS

Lio The Two-Legged Lion

L io has two legs.
I t lives in the rainforest.
O ccasionally he likes to scratch at trees.

T he monkey that lives next to him is cheeky.
H e protects his monkey from predators.
E xtra tame, cute and furry.

T en years he has lived with the monkey.
W hen he goes and plays he roars!
O n the rainforest floor.
-
L io is very good at jumping.
E xtraordinary he is.
G igantic with his long claws.
G entle with the monkey because it is his friend.
E xcellent at fighting.
D ead mice is what he eats.

L io is the best.
I n the world.
O ther animals love him.
N othing is more helpful than Lio.

Jack Hunter (8)
Baltasound Junior High School, Shetland

Blueingo The Blue Flamingo

My peculiar pet is Blueingo.
She is a blue flamingo with a crown on her soft blue head.
She rides around on her red skateboard like a two-year-old trying to ride a bike.
Blueingo is a very tame pet who lives in a desert as blue as the sea.
She only eats blue things.
Anything else she will spit in your face like a llama.
She will do anything if you give her something blue.
She goes *slurp slurp slurp* when she drinks the blue bit of the rainbow.
But you haven't heard the best thing yet.
When she gets wet she changes colour, all the different colours.
Yellow, green, purple, red, orange, but not pink!
Never pink, she hates pink, like cats hate water.

She spews so much when she sees pink that she turns into spew.
But despite all that stuff, she is a marvellous beauty of a pet and you should definitely get one.

Kathryn Mouat (9)
Baltasound Junior High School, Shetland

Turbo Snake

Turbo Snake is the biggest snake in the world.
He can walk on his talons and glide with his wing
from tree to tree.
His tail was split in half in an accident which spins
around and helps him glide.
One day he crashed through a window in an
aeroplane factory.
The machine thought the snake was an aeroplane
so it put jet engines on his wings.
Now he can fly.
Turbo Snake is incredibly clever because he knows
when you miss your flight.
He's tame and will come and pick you up.
There is only one snake like this.
Everyone gives him cake as a thank you.
I think if you saw him you would say he is
extraordinary.

Jaxon Ellis McConnell Thomson (9)
Baltasound Junior High School, Shetland

Tod Astrocow

T od is a space Highland cow, as cute as an
O tter and as friendly as cotton candy.
D id you know he likes chips?

A nother thing is that his horns look like ripe
bananas, his
S pacesuit is bright blue, do you have a spacesuit
too?
T imbo-Jimbo is his best friend.
R ed pants he has and a big bag o' chips.
O ctopus is his least favourite food, random I
know!
C lever as a cat and
O h how he loves Harry Potter and wants to visit
Hogwarts.
W hy he lives in space is a mystery to us all.

Casey Thomason (11)
Baltasound Junior High School, Shetland

Paul The Platy

P aul is as long as a giraffe's neck.
A nd he stays in a shipwreck.
U sually he leaves a mark wherever he goes.
L ike an alien he has three toes.

T ea is his favourite drink.
H e does not blink.
E -mail is how he talks to his friends.

P aul has fun in his dens.
L ast he plays on his PS4
A nd one of his friends comes to the door.
T hey play from day until night.
Y ou better watch out, they bite!

Hayden Thomson (8)
Baltasound Junior High School, Shetland

Mayor Destroy

Mayor Destroy is as yellow as a banana.
He has a goon called Parry the platypus.
He is two-headed.
Mayor Destroy used to be a good mayor named Troy.
Then a robber put money in his pocket
And the police chased him.
He thought it was fun
And turned into Mayor Destroy.
He has a belt as green as grass.
He has different kinds of bags for different banks he robs.
He can shrink past the police and the army.
He can also grow gigantic
As big as Godzilla and King Kong combined.

Corey Thomason (9)
Baltasound Junior High School, Shetland

Kim K Corgi

K im K Corgi is a very colourful corgi.

I ce cream is her favourite food.

M int chocolate chip... Mmm, so good!

K hloé K Corgi is her best friend.

C ooper the crocodile tries to eat Kim.

O h yeah, forgot to tell you, she doesn't like Kourtney K Corgi.

R aisins... Kourtney threw raisins at Kim.

G igi Mento dyes Kim's fur different colours.

I f you give Kim raisins she will scratch you like a tiger.

Alana Gray (10)
Baltasound Junior High School, Shetland

Sly Wolf

S ly Wolf is a peculiar pet.

L iving in the rainforest with snakes.

Y ou cannot tame it with its dangerous bite that can kill you.

W all climb and talk and she can go.

O ver walls she goes.

L eaves and meat she eats, hunting for her prey

F or her babies she hides then jumps to catch her prey.

Elizabeth Gunn (10)

Baltasound Junior High School, Shetland

Delphene The Jellyfish

D elphene is pink and scaly.

E veryone found her pretty scary.

L ots of glitter and hair dye.

P eople never make her cry.

H er microphone is on 'essential'.

E verybody says she's got potential.

N obody finds her scary anymore.

E very concert the crowd goes 'roar'!

Kirstie Thomson (10)

Baltasound Junior High School, Shetland

My Pet, Paul

My pet, Paul, is very bald.
He is as big as a whale and as tall as a giraffe.
He is really strong with his super stretch.
He lives in the ocean but can go on land.
He is extraordinary because he is big and long.
Paul is very ferocious but he is friendly to me.
He does my shopping at Morrisons whilst drinking beer.

Jamie Page (11)
Baltasound Junior High School, Shetland

Sharon The Snail

S haron is a snail, a very special snail.

H er best friend, Amanda, taught her how to sail.

A manda likes to walk to the shop.

R arely Sharon will walk but she mainly teleports.

O live oil stops her from getting warts.

N ever try to fight Sharon because she has super strength.

Dannielle Witt (11)
Baltasound Junior High School, Shetland

Match

M atch is a magic duck and he is messy.

A nother thing about him is he can talk.

T hen at night he uses magic to create a magic staff.

C atch is his favourite game.

H e looks like a duck but he wears a blue pair of shoes and a big bow tie.

Alexa Witt (8)
Baltasound Junior High School, Shetland

Jimmy The Banana

Jimmy is a pet banana that has a pet llama.
It likes to walk around straight through town.
My banana has a nice cool bandana.
My banana likes to dance with his llama.
You should pick my poem
Or it will turn into a ticking time bomb.

Joseph Thomson (10)
Baltasound Junior High School, Shetland

Parry The Platypus' Life

P arry works for Mayor Destroy.

A t a bank they rob it all.

R obbers they both are.

R un from the police to their secret lair as fast as cheetahs.

Y ay, they got away! Time for pizza to celebrate.

Ayva Witt (10)
Baltasound Junior High School, Shetland

Skate-Fox

There is this one fox
In our street.
He lives in a box.
But when I sit down to eat,
He zooms over here
And takes a seat.
Then with some flare
And a tweet,
Off Skate-Fox goes across the square.

Neve Priest (11)
Baltasound Junior High School, Shetland

Chefin Loves Cookies All Day Long

Chefin the sausage dog loves to cook chocolate chip cookies and dip them in milk.

He stinks of cookies all day long.

He fries his pineapple pie and cries.

He burnt his biscuit badly and cried all day long.

He was in a very deep sleep until he heard a big bang!

He jumped out of his bed with a big scream and had the biggest fright.

The big bang was... his owner.

His owner gave him a big juicy steak.

He put it in a lake because Chefin didn't like the steak, he likes cookies.

So Chefin flew away with his cookies on his back.

He came back with a friend called Mack.

He had a lack of sleep.

They cooked cookies all day long.

They ate them on a crate and they had a cookie and they became colourful.

Sophia Volder (11)

Carbrain Primary School, Cumbernauld

Maddie's Peculiar Day

Maddie was very mad because her muddle puddle dried out.
She flew into a ramp and leapt into a lamp.
She fell down and pulled a frown.
She flew all the way home and saw her owner in a deep sleep.
She leapt onto the bed and licked Josy then lights flicked.
Josy made her bed and got on Maddie's back
And flew into the deep, scary, frightening night.
As the stars glistened in the deep dark sky Josy fell off.
Maddie caught her just in time with her horn, whilst eating corn.
Josy was very grateful.
Josy leaned on the bannister and screamed.
She fell through and Maddie was asleep.
Thankfully her dad caught her.
Maddie laughed and everything was good.

Ellie Swarbrick (10)

Carbrain Primary School, Cumbernauld

My Amazing Pets

N aughty when she climbs the curtains.
A nnoying when she scratches me, ow!
L azy. She's incredibly lazy.
A mazing at sleeping.

P awsome at running.
O rdinary at taking up most of the space on the couch.
P erfect at sleeping.
P uptastic at barking at the door.
Y ucky when she is in the mud.

When I get out my two wild pets start to shout.
They run around the roundabout.
They cross the road on a cockroach.
They go to the house and see a mouse
And throw it out the window.
I forgot, my cat eats my toes!

Nieve Elliot (10)
Carbrain Primary School, Cumbernauld

Dragog

Bill the dragon flew by a helicopter.
He clawed it and it went down.
He was eating when his wolf friend came.
They played for an hour then the wolf howled loud.
His pack came and started to attack the dragon.
The dragon fought back.
The dragon killed five of the wolves.
The rest ran far away into the woods.
The friendly wolf was not friendly.
The wolves killed a lion, a male,
And it was a dad of three.
The dragon, Bill, in the day he was a dog
When it was day his name was Zeus.
He had lots of love by his family.
His family loved him lots.

Robbie Allan (11)
Carbrain Primary School, Cumbernauld

The Scaly Thief

Taz is my peculiar pet.
During the day he is a normal iguana
But at night he is a scaly thief.
When I go to sleep he leaves
And steals from someone.
I have watches, toys and other stuff.
I went to one of my neighbours.
He was playing with Taz.
My neighbour said that he had been losing
watches from his collection and that caught my
attention.
I looked at my neighbour and then looked back at
Taz.
He had a necklace and I liked it.
It was a black chain with a black and silver
motorbike.

Cole Smith (10)
Carbrain Primary School, Cumbernauld

Dangerous Peppa Shrek

P awsome when it is sleeping.
E vil when it is angry.
P eppa Shrek is pretty when it is wild.
P eppa Shrek will claw you when it is ferocious.
A dorable when it is dangerous.

S assy when it is furry and tiny.
H ere is a clawed eye Peppa Shrek.
R un out the door when you open it.
E mpty in the shower.
K arate Peppa Shrek.

Kelsie Robertson (10)

Carbrain Primary School, Cumbernauld

The Magical Bunny Dog

One day I adopted a dog.
She was cute and furry
But one night she jumped so high
And I realised she had a bunny tail
And she started to fly.
I was amazed when I saw some really glittery dust.
I always wanted a computer
And a bunny dog made me one.
I never told Mum
Because she would not believe me.
I love my bunny dog so much.

Emilia Kubinska (10)
Carbrain Primary School, Cumbernauld

Squoop The Tabby Dragon

One day I woke up in my mum's pizzeria,
But just then I got the best idea.
I grabbed my cat, but not in fright,
But when the moon cracked through and stole the light.
We got up to the shadows so high,
Yes, my cat could actually fly!
She was black in shadow with pieces of magma.
She might be a female but is still the alpha.

Noah Lamley (11)
Carbrain Primary School, Cumbernauld

The Flying Rabbit

I need to tame my rabbit before she flies too high.
You may find this peculiar but she can fly in the sky.
She may be cute and furry but don't let that fool you.
My marvellous bunny can be very funny.
When her claws come out at night they can give you such a fright.
She is just so extraordinary I like to hold her tight.

Rhys McPhee (11)
Carbrain Primary School, Cumbernauld

The Big Fat Cat

There was a big fat cat called Night.
He was as black as a bat and as fat as a rat.
He sat on the mat to go for a big long cat nap
But did you know he was a sassy, lazy, fat cat.
In the night he turned into a bright knight.
When it turned back into day
He was the fat cat he always was!

Abbie McGeachy (10)
Carbrain Primary School, Cumbernauld

My Very Hungry Cat

One day my cat ate the table
And came to me and looked at me.
In a second he ate my bed covers.
I woke up and I wanted to walk downstairs
But my cat ate the stairs.
When I called my cat he came
But he came by walking to me on the wall and
roof.

Milaniia Iekimova (10)
Carbrain Primary School, Cumbernauld

Catman

My pet is as tall as a tree.
My pet is as naughty as a bee.
My pet is as shiny as the sun.
My pet is like a bun.
My pet shouts like a speaker.
My pet is as hot as a heater.
My pet is as scary as a bat cave.
My pet is like a lion, how brave!
My pet is as funny as a town.
My pet is as busy as a town.
My pet is as disgusting as Godzilla.
My pet is as silly as a tortilla.
My pet is as happy as Aston Villa.
My pet is a tall, old tree.
My pet is a naughty bee.
My pet is a shiny sun.
My pet is a bun.
My pet is a loud speaker.
My pet is a hot heater.

My pet is a scary bat cave.
My pet is a lion, how brave!
Of course, my pet is Catman.

Bradley Samuriwo (10)
Forest Hills Primary School, Rugeley

The Shnowder

My pet is a tall cash pile.
My pet is a car going a mile.
My pet is a tall tree.
My pet is a huge knee.
My pet is a big house.
My pet is never a small mouse.

My pet is a nice bulging red.
My pet hates having a bed.
My pet is harder than a nail.
My pet hates slow garden snails.
My pet is a hard beast
But you can't join in on the feast.

My pet is a fast car.
My pet uses pull-up bars.
My pet is a luscious treater.
My pet is sometimes a hard-beating beater.
My pet is a fierce cheetah.
My pet is never to me a horrible beater.
My pet is a shnowder.

Lewis Jackson (10)
Forest Hills Primary School, Rugeley

Minochog

My pet is as weird as me.
My pet is as buzzed as a bee.
My pet is as strong as a gorilla.
My pet is as tall as Godzilla.
My pet is as gorgeous as a puppy.
My pet is as wonderful as a cookie.
My pet is as yummy as electric wires!
My pet is as dangerous as a fire.
My pet is as bright as the sun.
My pet is funnier than fun.
My pet is as hungry as me.
My pet is as still as a tree.
My pet is as long as a nail.
My pet is better than a fail.
My pet is deadlier than Deadly Bo.
My pet is prettier than pretty.

Cameron Hulley (10)
Forest Hills Primary School, Rugeley

The Phichick

My pet is as hot as lava.
My pet is as white as snow.
My pet is as blue as drama.
My pet is as brave as a bow.

My pet is as loud as a whale.
My pet is as quiet as a mouse.
My pet is as happy as a male.
My pet is as big as a house.

My pet is as heavy as a tree.
My pet is as colourful as a rainbow.
My pet is as kind as me.
My pet is as sticky as dough.
My pet's beak is as hard as a nail.
My pet is of course, a phichick.

Cealan Millerchip (10)
Forest Hills Primary School, Rugeley

Devilfish Cat

Devilfish Cat is a peculiar pet.
It's as rogue as a rhino
And as clever as a vet.
As quick as an octopus shooting through the sea.
As quiet as a ninja that no one can see.
As silly as a squirrel.
As round as a hound.
As terrible as a pterodactyl flying around.
As cheeky as a monkey screaming in the zoo.
As cool as a cucumber and as green.
To others, Devilfish Cat is a peculiar pet.
An unusual animal you won't soon forget.

Lewis Gill (9)
Forest Hills Primary School, Rugeley

The Leopareindeer

The leopareindeer is a peculiar pet.
It's as big as a hippo.
As clever as a vet.
As fast as a lion, shooting through the trees.
As quiet as a mouse, that squeaks by its tree.
As sour as a lemon.
As hard as a rock.
As loud as popcorn in a pot.
As cheeky as a monkey.
As busy as a bee
That is that busy that it has no time for tea.
The leopareindeer is a peculiar pet.
An unusual animal you will not forget.

Destiny-May Davies-Jackson (9)
Forest Hills Primary School, Rugeley

Dragon Bug

My pet is as dangerous as space.
My pet is as open as a door.
My pet is as sharp as a claw.
My pet is as fun as grace.
My pet is as vicious as a snake.
My pet is as reliable as a bug.
My pet is as angry as an old hag.
My pet is as long as a lake.
My pet is as cold as the sea.
My pet is as tall as a house.
My pet is as small as a mouse.
My pet speaks German to me.

My pet is, of course, a dragon bug!

Maisie Clasper (11)
Forest Hills Primary School, Rugeley

Dat

My pet is as tall as a tree.
Likes to mess with a bee.
My pet is as slow as a snail.
Doesn't let people cut its nails.

My pet is as loud as a tiger.
Always takes my fiver.
Sometimes as quiet as a mouse
But doesn't fit in a house.

My pet doesn't know what to do.
Is always going to the loo.
My pet sleeps on its tail
But is as strong as a whale.
My pet is, of course, a dat!

Amy-Lee Green (11)
Forest Hills Primary School, Rugeley

The Fairy Flying Cat

The fairy flying cat is a peculiar pet.
She's as jumpy as a monkey,
And as clever as a vet.

As quick as a shark chasing blood.
As rare as a dinosaur.
As dirty as mud.
As cool as a cucumber.
Her fairy dust will make your mind wonder.

As round as a hound.
As silly as a bird flying around.

The fairy flying cat is a peculiar pet.
An unusual pet you won't soon forget.

Laycie Grant (9)
Forest Hills Primary School, Rugeley

Big Chungus

My pet is taller than a tree.
My pet's footsteps make a ring
For he is 76' 3".
My pet will always sing.
He's Big Chungus.
He's a big chunky boy.
He's like a big fungus.
He fills himself with joy.
"I eat people who fail my checks."
My pet is as full as a thing.
My pet plays with his sticks.
My pet eats everything.
My pet is, of course, Big Chungus.

Antoni Kopaniecki (10)
Forest Hills Primary School, Rugeley

Flying Frog

The flying frog is a peculiar pet.
It's as funny as a fan.
As clever as a net.
As green as a tree.
As angry as a bat.
As tired as a bee.
As playful as a cat.

As sweet as candy.
As small as money.
As sour as a lemon.
As big as a book.
The flying frog is a peculiar pet.
An unusual animal
You won't soon forget.

Gabriella Azace-Berzina (9)
Forest Hills Primary School, Rugeley

Llama Elephant

The llama elephant is a peculiar pet.
It is as smart as an octopus.
As hot as a kettle.
As small as a snail.
As big as an elephant.
As amazing as an octopus.
As buzzy as a bee.
As bossy as a bat.
As crazy as a cat.
As scary as a wolf.
As brown as Brownies.
As young as a baby.
As fast as a flamingo.
As blue as the sky.

Marina Ryan (8)
Forest Hills Primary School, Rugeley

Dino Dog

As tall as an enormous dino dog.
As small as a dog's body.
As tiny as a dog's head like a Chihuahua.
My dino dog has three legs.
My dog sounds like scratches from a dino dog.
My pet scares people away with his dino roar.
My dino dog cannot break his arms or legs
because they are made out of bones.
My dino dog has four whole heads together.

Ryley Harvey (9)
Forest Hills Primary School, Rugeley

My Flat Cat

The flat cat is a peculiar pet.
She lives in my flat.
Drinks water out of the bubbly bath.
Cleo eats last night's pizza on a bright yellow mat.
Purrs as soft as a Lamborghini
And hides like a genie.
Sleeps so still at times on the window sill and
blinds.
My flat cat is a peculiar pet.
An unusual animal
You will never forget.

Lacey Barnett (8)
Forest Hills Primary School, Rugeley

Crazy Pet

My pet has a big buggy smile.
My pet licks a tile.
My pet cooks in a pot
Then eats it hot.
My pet's body is the size of a kitten.
My pet wears a mitten.
My pet barks at pans.
My pet wears fake tan.
My pet plays with a rat.
My pet wears a hat.
My pet is as hot as a kettle.
My pet is as pretty as a petal.

Maizie Eppy (9)
Forest Hills Primary School, Rugeley

My Chickilliger

My pet is as small as a pale chicken.
My pet is as cute as a sleeping baby.
My pet is as strange as a talking tree.
My pet is as light as a buzzy bee.
My pet is as fluffy as a mega Frank.
My pet is as deadly as freezing water.
My pet is as fast as a cheetah.
My pet is as friendly as a doggy.
My pet is a chickilliger.

Owen Jones (11)
Forest Hills Primary School, Rugeley

Holly The Hamster

It's Holly the hamster, a peculiar pet.
It's as fast as a cheetah.
As hungry as a lion.
It sleeps all day, all night too.
It's as cute as a baby
And less scary than a dinosaur.
The cutest thing on Earth
Besides my baby sister.
The hamster is a peculiar pet.
An unusual animal you won't forget.

Aaliyah Millerchip (7)
Forest Hills Primary School, Rugeley

Owo Cat

Here is my Owo Cat.
He is a very strange pet.
He is as tiny as a rat.
Oh, he is my Owo Cat.

As fast as a flash.
Then as slow as a snail.
As dumb as a beetle,
Chasing his tail.

As pale as a peach,
But he does love the beach.
He is as cheeky as a monkey,
Who is very, very chunky.

Demi Grant (8)
Forest Hills Primary School, Rugeley

Art Rat

My pet is a rat with an apron.
Like a bat with a stain on.
Plus he has a big brush on his back.
He goes squawk, quack and finally whack!
What it does is unusual because it draws with no flaws.
It paints with an unusual taint.
He eats many types of meat
And beet, seats and feet.

My pet is Art Rat.

Dexter Clark (10)
Forest Hills Primary School, Rugeley

The Long Cat

The long cat is a peculiar pet.
It's as rogue as a rhino.
As clever as a vet.

As cheeky as a monkey screaming in the zoo.
As silly as a snake.
As round as a hound.
As terrible as a pterodactyl flying around.

The long cat is a peculiar pet.
An unusual animal you soon won't forget.

Marita Bolsakova (9)
Forest Hills Primary School, Rugeley

The Clat

My pet is as old as a nail.
My pet is as clever as a whale.
My pet is as happy as a male.
My pet's jumps are like at a fair.

My pet is as old as a nan.
My pet is as big as a man.
My pet is in front of a fan.
My pet's head is as small as a can.

My pet is a clown mixed with a cat.

Sonny Jones (10)
Forest Hills Primary School, Rugeley

Fluff Pig

My pet is fun.
It loves a bit of chocolate bun.
It is as cuddly as a sumo.
It is as fluffy as Elmo.
It watches clean memes.
It plays video games in teams.
It never dies.
It is scared of flies.
It speaks English.
He never speaks gibberish.
My pet of course is a fluff pig!

Jamie Skerten (10)
Forest Hills Primary School, Rugeley

The Coffee Sheep

The coffee sheep is a peculiar pet.
It's as small as a mouse.
As clever as a vet.

As quick as a cheetah shooting through the sea.
As quiet as a ninja that no one can see.

As silly as a squirrel.
As fluffy as a cloud.
As golden as a star flying around.

Lola Barnet (9)
Forest Hills Primary School, Rugeley

Simile Poem

My pet is as vicious as a T-rex.
My pet is as tall as a tree.
My pet is as playful as a lion.
My pet is as brave as Godzilla.
My pet is as smart as a baby.
My pet is as confused as a bee.
My pet is as long as a tree flat on the ground.
My pet is, of course, a T-raptor.

Harley Butler-Cockayne (10)
Forest Hills Primary School, Rugeley

Mega Pat

My pet is a cat.
He is as fluffy as a mat.
He is as tall as a skyscraper.
He is as white as paper.
My pet is as scary as a deep, dark cave.
My pet is as wet as a wave.
My pet is as bossy as Simon Cowell.
My pet is as deep as a well.
Of course, my pet is Mega Pat.

Brandon Samuriwo (10)
Forest Hills Primary School, Rugeley

Dragon

As clever as a monkey.
As lazy as a sloth.
As kind as a donkey.
As naughty as a goth.
As tall as the grass.
As small as an ant.
As smiley as sass.
As smelly as pants.
As silly as a duck.
As quiet as an ant.
As old as a book.
As funny as a cat.

Ashleigh Davies (11)
Forest Hills Primary School, Rugeley

The Shark Duck

The shark duck is a peculiar pet.
It's as fast as a duck
And as quick as a dog.
It's as hungry as a hippo.
As clever as a rat.
As funny as a monkey.
As bossy as a bat.

The shark duck is a peculiar pet.
An unusual animal you won't forget.

Vinnie Nolan (8)
Forest Hills Primary School, Rugeley

The Goblin Phoenix

The goblin phoenix is a peculiar pet.
It is as fast as a werewolf that eats human flesh.
It is as fiery as a flaming fire.
It is as clever as a snake.
It is as naughty as a lion that is eating its prey.
The goblin phoenix is a peculiar pet
You won't soon forget.

Kieran Baker (9)
Forest Hills Primary School, Rugeley

Megacat

My pet is as tall as a whale.
My pet is not very pale.
My pet has blue dreadlocks.
My pet has not got chickenpox.
My pet plays with a rope.
My pet likes soap.
My pet has a top hat.
My pet likes to be called Pat.
My pet is, of course, a megacat.

Harley Eppy (11)
Forest Hills Primary School, Rugeley

The Tiger Shark

The tiger shark is a peculiar pet.
As stripy as a zebra
Who is as busy as a beaver.
He swims very fast.
He always has a blast.
His fin is as big as a giant's chin.
As noisy as a cat purring like a car.
Last seen swimming in the pool.

Lewis Hulley (8)
Forest Hills Primary School, Rugeley

Jack The Transforming Bird

The transforming bird is a peculiar pet.
It can fly up in the air
And at night it turns into a fish.
It can swim very far
And can eat little fish.
It can go back into the air
To look for rats to eat for dinner.

Jayden Jackson (8)
Forest Hills Primary School, Rugeley

Crocodile Unicorn

The crocodile unicorn is a peculiar pet.
It's as big as a buffalo.
As clever as a vet.

As big as an elephant.
As silly as a clown
Who isn't very funny.

Lailah-Rose Jenkins (8)
Forest Hills Primary School, Rugeley

The Little Puppy, Roco

The little puppy is a peculiar pet.
It's as good as a horse.
As loud as sheep.
As fast as a mouse.
As small as a little spider.
As tall as a tree.

Reegan Jackson (8)
Forest Hills Primary School, Rugeley

Dog Mouse

The big dog has a little mouse's body.
She loves cheese so much.
The dog mouse loves to play outside
And the mouse and dog love each other.

Perri Haste (7)
Forest Hills Primary School, Rugeley

War Crocodile

As strong as a tank.
As brave as a soldier.
As big as a megalodon.
Swims fast like a piranha.
As dangerous as a god.

Robert Chipernea (10)

Forest Hills Primary School, Rugeley

Stinky Dragon

D ragon is stinky.
R oaring when the dragon is mad
A nd when he gets tickled.
G o dragon, roar!
O n his bike.
N o, naughty, stinky dragon.

Harry Murphy
Kingsdown School, Southend-On-Sea

Oz The Fluffy Cat

C at found a hat

A nd a small can.

T he cat fell in the hat.

Toby Ward (14)

Kingsdown School, Southend-On-Sea

Silly Dog

Dog...
Angry.
Big.
Sleepy.
Stinky.

Sam Kempen (14)
Kingsdown School, Southend-On-Sea

Lion

Lion...
Scary.
Glittery.
Stinky.

Eddie Lewis
Kingsdown School, Southend-On-Sea

Sleepy Shark And Noisy Whale

Shark...
Sleepy.
Whale...
Noisy.

James Beaumont
Kingsdown School, Southend-On-Sea

Super Dogs

S uper and brave, he's not even scared of a cave.

U nique and tough. Super Dogs has had enough.

P owerful as a rhino he can also break through a window.

E xtreme and rad, he is very mad.

R ude and bad the pets were so sad.

D own and up the dog jumped, all of a sudden he felt some bumps.

O utstanding and magical the dog acts like a normal animal.

G reat, his behaviour changed and the pets were outraged.

S trong and happy, Super Dogs is so scruffy.

Great Celestine (9)

St Joseph's Catholic Primary School, Deptford

Demny The Dazzling Duck

There was a shy duck named Demny
She was really smelly
She had no friends, never went to bed
And spent her time with her teddy.

There was a dazzling duck
That had lots of bucks
But suddenly had no luck!

Demny was unlucky
She had no money
Slept on the streets, gave her dog some meat
Then one day found a buddy.

There was a fat duck
Who ate lots of cake
But never liked to bake
She spent all her luck on food
And always had an attitude.

Demny the glorious duck liked to sing
And she always wore exclusive bling!

Demny the dazzling duck
Nearly got hit by a tremendous truck
And now people think she's yuck.

Caitlyn Torsu (9)
St Joseph's Catholic Primary School, Deptford

June The Jazzy Puppy

June the jazzy puppy, my personal pup,
Heals me when I'm hurt with just a single touch.
Wears a diamond sparkling dress
Then goes to the dance floor,
When she stops dancing everybody screams for more.
She dances like a queen and flies in the night with me.
But she's my pet, June, that's just her personality.
I don't know how she sleeps all through the day,
And is awake all through the night,
But she's my favourite pet,
She's mine, all mine.

Michal Kamau (10)

St Joseph's Catholic Primary School, Deptford

Samy The Snake

This is Samy the snake...
Let me show you what he can make.
He can make super shoes
That make you super swift.
He can make colourful clothes.
When you wear them they shine like the sun.
He can make plentiful pizzas.
With every piece you feel peaceful.
He makes delicious spaghetti
Which is fit for the heavens.
This is why he's truly the best,
Better than the rest!

Jordan Okeke (10)
St Joseph's Catholic Primary School, Deptford

Smart And Happy Cat

My smart and happy cat likes to wear a hat.
Normally she sits on my mat
But today she is sitting on my sofa with a hat on.
She is a very clever cat, she also likes hearts.
She also knows all her times tables.
She does not like rats and spiders.
She also has friends that are cats.
This is my pet cat.
My family does not like the cat
But I still love it.

David Okebu (10)
St Joseph's Catholic Primary School, Deptford

The Space Dog

I went to space.
I learnt how to float.
I found a black hole.
It said hello.
It gave me a cool, cute dog.
A super-duper cool, cute dog.
The cool, cute dog and I went all around space.
We floated all around space.
I learnt how to love a dog.
I learnt how to adore a dog.
My lesson today is how to take care of a super-duper, cool, cute dog.

Leslie Salinas Laserna (10)
St Joseph's Catholic Primary School, Deptford

Gary The Whale

Once I moved house and my family found a huge
fish tank in the centre.
We didn't know what do so we bought a whale
and put it inside.
But something happened to the whale...
He grew legs and walked.
The whale's name is Garry
And he can jump really high.
It can almost fly.
Gary can read
But I'm still teaching him how to wee.

Caleb Luyimbazi (10)

St Joseph's Catholic Primary School, Deptford

The Puppy

Today I got a puppy.
I named her Willow.
The first night was okay I guess.
When I went to sleep Willow went to the woods.
It was 1am and I woke up.
I was going to get water but then I saw Willow,
She was not in her black gloomy bed.
When I found her I saw her turn into a wolf.
We went home and went to bed.

Selina Sarpong (10)
St Joseph's Catholic Primary School, Deptford

Sausage Dog

Sausage Dog, Sausage Dog,
Oh boy, you're a cheeky one.
Sausage Dog, Sausage Dog,
Oh boy, aren't you a hungry one.
Scoffing down your biscuits and your food,
Never getting tired,
Always playing, playing.
Sausage Dog, Sausage Dog,
Oh boy, aren't you a handful!

Manasse Mfutila (9)
St Joseph's Catholic Primary School, Deptford

Hamstercorns Are The Best

Hamstercorn, Hamstercorn,
You are the best.
Half unicorn and half hamster,
Nobody can detest.
You're beautiful and kind.
The best animal in the world.
You're dangerous, cute and clever.
Wild, colourful and sassy all at the same time.

Hephzibah Akinbosoye (10)
St Joseph's Catholic Primary School, Deptford

Guinea Fly

Guinea Fly, go so high over the night sky.
He twitches, he itches, he eats lots of pie.
He visits penguins, he visits dolphins,
Over the sea, over the square.
He goes on the news,
He goes everywhere!
He is very clean but sometimes ends up in the washing machine.
All he eats is broccoli and cheese.
He squawks a lot, he eats from a pot.
If you want to do a fly race get ready to be damaged.
Bam! Run! You'll turn into a nun!
You'll be praying you didn't do that on that day
And they hadn't taken you away.
Shoot! The TV's on, listen to the guinea pig song!
Sing along! And when the popcorn is finished
Grab some more 'cause we're still not finished.
He's very friendly but I don't pick him up,
All you will get is a big bite on your arm.
Now he says bye, fly!

Jessica Miro (7)
The Village Prep School, Belsize Park

My Butterfly

My butterfly is very cute,
Although sometimes she wanders down the
garbage chute.
Her wings are soft white bread,
And very cosy when she is tucked in bed!
All the other butterflies are shocked to see
A butterfly who kind of looks like a tree!
Butterfly's appetite is some tuna and cheese,
But she sometimes says, "I should have nectar, not
eat these!"
I think that Butterfly is funny,
Because she often joins the bees and has honey.

Iman Farid (7)

The Village Prep School, Belsize Park

A Clever Cat

Once there was a cat that lived under a flat
And slept happily on a mat.
One day she found a kitten on her bed
And she chose to look after it so she made it a
bed.

What a peculiar cat!
She goes fishing with a bat
And she likes sleeping with a rat!
She cooks homemade meals
With a pan and a shield!

This clever and peculiar cat is Lilly,
My most favourite animal in the land!

Victoria Mantzouki (8)
The Village Prep School, Belsize Park

Posh Plumbing Pug

Very posh Plumbing Pug works all day and night
To finish Poor Pup's house at the dead of night.
Poor Pup cries in sorrow 'cause his house is not yet done
But tired Plumbing Pug is nothing but a bum.
When Plumbing Pug is finishing Poor Pup is so light,
He flies away on a plump white cloud in delight, in the dead of night.

Alina Alexeeva (9)

The Village Prep School, Belsize Park

Spencer The Spaghetti-Loving Squirrel

There once was a squirrel
That loved to wriggle and run
Until he saw a hot dog bun.
Then he ate spaghetti,
And turned into a yeti.
He turned back into a squirrel
But he refused to run and jiggle.
He ate more and more spaghetti
But he became all sweaty.
He had lots more,
And began to roar!

Arabella McGregor (10)
The Village Prep School, Belsize Park

The Lime Green

My dino has puffy pink wings
And when I ride her I smell her lime scent.
My dino is always ready for fun,
It's gonna be funny.
She likes doing magic tricks,
It's gonna be funny.
She's as happy as a rainbow
And smells like a new pair of shoes.
She is as exciting as a cloud
And as pretty as a model.

Daisy Wilson (8)
Weavervale Primary School, Frodsham

Mine And Bucky's Beach Day

Me and Bucky hung out at the beach
Then sat down and ate a peach.
In a flash we ate then we hung out a bit more
But then it started to get late
So we headed back home and had some cake.
After we had the cake we headed to bed
And dreamed about having a strawberry shake.

Sofia Clare (9)
Weavervale Primary School, Frodsham

Dinosaur Poem

D angling bunny ears.

I nteresting, incredible.

N eat and tidy.

O f course she's purple and elegant of course.

S tubby, see-through wings.

A s purple as lavender.

U nusual and

R eally see-through wings.

Melissa Winter (8)

Weavervale Primary School, Frodsham

Emgranster

E nergetic

M arvellous

G angster

R eally cool like a rock star

A s I walked Emgranster started performing

N ice

S tar

T all neck

E xciting

R ules the world!

Gracie Garner (8)

Weavervale Primary School, Frodsham

Ellie Dog

Ellie Dog is marvellous and feathery.
Ellie Dog is clever and tiny.
Ellie Dog is lazy and wild.
Ellie Dog is messy, slimy and colourful.
It has a long trunk.
Those legs are funny.
Ellie Dog is big and tall.

Jamie O'Grady
Weavervale Primary School, Frodsham

The Dograteldipe

Dograteldipe is one of a kind.
I am the only one with him.
Opens his wings like a flying pterodactyl.
Giant and beautiful.

Luke McCabe-Boutrus (9)
Weavervale Primary School, Frodsham

Strangle

He can climb,
He can strangle,
He is the perfect snake
To handle his mission.

Thomas Fairfield (8)

Weavervale Primary School, Frodsham

Boring Budgie

Bonnie the budgie was a boring bud,
She wouldn't even like to go in the mud,
Bonnie didn't even move when she saw a ladybird!

The owner said to the budgie to go over there,
But the budgie didn't move, she didn't dare,
The owner murmured, "She is as scary as a nightmare!"
But the budgie didn't care!
She would just stay in her lair,
All she was doing was sitting in that chair!
She was the opposite of a hare!

The owner thought: *I don't think Bonnie does eat,*
Well, luckily she doesn't eat meat,
But she only stays on that seat!
She doesn't even react when I give her a treat!

The owner wanted Bonnie to spend time with her,
forever or for a day,
But she thought Bonnie was not going to do it,
even for a day,
The last time she moved around was last May,

May went away and it is August today,
She will never change, nor will she obey,
In the night, the owner doesn't even see her lay!

Iqra Chaudhry (10)
White Court School, Great Notley

Fox Magical Fox

Fox Magical Fox
Who has every power in the world
It's her
Her name's Fairy
With purple fur, with a tragic past.

Oh no!
She can create the end of the world
But she is very fast
Like a racing car.

X-ray the tail
You see electric trails
You see that the tail
Is very high-powered
I didn't know that it was a problem.

When I got her
She was cute but too hard to control
So I let her go
But I didn't know
That it was the end of the world for me.

Bang! Crash!
Everything went flying into each other
Oh no!
Everyone is blaming her for it
And it is my fault.

They locked her up
But I know she is too clever for it
She escaped
Bang! Crash!
Fox Magical Fox.

It is not her fault
She can't control her powers
So misunderstood
So sad for her
I need to help her
She is a tsunami of worries.

Austeja Andrulyte (10)
White Court School, Great Notley

Flake

I have a pet named Flake,
Who is scared of lakes.
He's a spiked dog/dragon,
But can't pull a wagon.

He throws the sweet wrapper
Then gets it only to make it flatter.
He likes to eat sweets
But vegetables he just can't eat.

At bedtime, he sleeps messily,
But at ballet he dances gracefully.
He hugs his teddy
But tightly squeezes it when ready.

The spikes don't hurt him
But the Xs cross over him.
His wings spread
Then his head gets a pet.

Sadly he can't cry
But he can definitely try.
He has a dark spike under his eye,
But makes it normal when he tries, tries, tries.

Oh my pet is glorious,
But secretly victorious.
He has an invisible crown,
But it can't be seen by the town.

Samuel Weeks (10)
White Court School, Great Notley

Dazzly Dondeablo

Dondeablo is the star of the shows,
Once or twice a day he glows.
Never wants to hide.
Dondeablo has never lied.
Every time he eats
A servant comes, who is called Pete.
Beware, he's very moody.
He has a friend called Judy.
Dondeablo met someone called Flo
Then they went on a row.
They had some rice
And caught some mice.
You think he's kind
But he will drive you out of your mind.

Dondeablo is white and brown.
Dondeablo is never seen with a frown.
He has an outfit for every day
And a special one for the 12th of May.
He is a true peculiar pet
But you just don't know it yet.

Dondeablo shone bright
And was never called right
And was never called wrong.

Emily Oliver (9)
White Court School, Great Notley

Flying Fred

Furry Fred is here to save the day,
He's coming to town to come and play,
With a flap of his wings
And the wind in his face,
The tiny guinea pig was in a race.
Would he be on time to rescue the mice
From the wild cat that was full of lice?

Furry Fred is here to save the day,
Creatures move out of the way!
With his laser eyes
And his razor teeth,
He has fought off the clawed cat
And has saved the mice who are now on a mat.

Furry Fred is here to save the day,
It's quite warm in the middle of May,
He's on his way home,
That's in the middle of Rome,
And now he's on the kitchen floor,
Next to the playroom door,
Eating spinach and parsley galore!

Lauren Elizabeth Sibley (9)
White Court School, Great Notley

Wander Sausage

I like sausages
But one day my Sausage went for a walk.
It went across the street to the butcher's shop
And took every sausage it could find.
At first I thought it was saving them
But then had them for lunch.
I had a closer look and realised it was my dog.
I love my dog even though it looks like a sausage.
I love my dog and luckily I didn't have him for
lunch.

The next day I had two sausages for lunch
And I made sure I locked my door so my dog
couldn't get out.
It's been a while since I've seen my dog.
I looked everywhere but still nothing
Until I found him behind my clock.
I love my dog and luckily I found him before he was
too stuck.

Jack Clow (9)
White Court School, Great Notley

Super Brandie

S mart, soft and has a good feeling for not eating mice.

U nder the clouds above Land's Point.

P oofing invisible bombs that will blow everyone's minds.

E rasing your sad memories with happy ones.

R iding under the clouds, meowing his way through.

B randie is very brandy, he is the talk of his town.

R andy is a short way of saying Brandie's name.

A nd has super vision and eyes.

N okia bricks are not as strong as him.

D efinitely gonna win the super cat competition.

I nvisible cape for stopping crime.

E ventually at the top he marks the world a special plot.

James Smith (10)
White Court School, Great Notley

DJ Perfect Panda

DJ Perfect Panda likes to relax on the sofa
Whilst drinking Coca-Cola
He is a snuggly pet to have
And he likes to listen to beach waves.

Perfect Panda is messy
When he is eating rainbow cake.
He gets you to bake 1,000 rainbow cakes
For him to have when he is hungry
And his favourite colour is rainbow.

If you could tell
DJ Perfect Panda is a DJ
He likes to show off his music
Everyone moves it and grooves it.

He is a cuddly panda
He is gigantic and cute
And he sometimes mutes.

DJ Perfect Panda is trying something new
But he gets shy and he tries not to cry
When everyone is watching.

Emily Coe (10)
White Court School, Great Notley

Watching, Wacky Waffles

He bounces, he leaps, he stands like a sheep,
He's watching, he's waiting, to come and be fed
While he stares dangerously in his messy king-sized bed.
If you come close whilst he's eating his roast carrots and bread,
He will dash up to you and sniff you instead.
If he is in a good mood he will get nervous and tinkle,
But if he is unhappy he will have a power snooze
Whilst his shiny claws twinkle.
If you are lucky he will be polite,
But if he is grumpy he will stay out of sight.
Then he will snuggle next to you
And stay happy all night.
Wacky Waffles can be nibbly but don't you fright!

Abigail Hodgson (10)
White Court School, Great Notley

My Soggy Poggy

Soggy Poggy is stinky,
I don't know if he has a pinky,
He always screams 'dinky'.

Soggy Poggy gets angry,
He hates his brother, Pangy,
He loves Haribo Tangy.

Soggy Poggy's friend is called Rank,
That's because he drives a tank,
He might do a flank.

Soggy Poggy smells like a ship,
But he doesn't like pips,
He might steal your chips.

Soggy Poggy loves his Twix,
But he prefers Weetabix,
He also likes the Grand Prix.

Soggy Poggy realises he's lost his eye,
As the night goes by,
But he has a nice chicken pie.

Matthew McGlone (10)
White Court School, Great Notley

The Strange Serpent

I have a snake,
His name is Jake.
He likes to bake,
Lots of cake.

He likes mice and steak,
Only if it's been baked.
Only in the afternoon,
He likes to play tunes.

With his scaly skin,
He likes to rest in the bin.
You may find him eating,
Or maybe seating.

He likes to hypnotise,
With his crazy button eyes.
He can move over 200km,
If he goes onward.

Legs go faster,
A tail of a spider.
Fangs to release venom,
And as sour as a lemon.

Fangs sharper than a tiger's tooth,
He is not scared of a camera booth!

Lauren J (10)
White Court School, Great Notley

Double Trouble

D own in the dogs' holes,

O ut come tonnes of moles.

U nder the sea you would always have a peek,

B elow my puppy's dirty feet.

L ying down in the pool,

E eek! My puppies have done a big poop!

T iny pups in the mud,

R elaxing while eating shrubs.

O utside in the wild,

U p in the sky it's mild.

B y the dogs' bed, they made a horrible mess,

L earning things in the dog school and eating things in the mess pool.

E eek! At the big dogs' hog pool we found one of Khloe's dog balls.

Gracie Card (9)
White Court School, Great Notley

My Lying Sausage Dog

I have a pet that's a sausage dog,
He can speak,
But every time he lies
His body grows.

His body gets longer
When he blames the next-door neighbour's cat
For the vase that he smashed.

He grows longer
When he lies that someone else ate all the treats.

His body grows when he lies
That someone else ate the post.

He grows longer when he says
He didn't scare the children.

His body stretches longer
When he says he didn't knock down the fridge.

And he runs away as he says
He doesn't need to go to the vets.

Dexter Michael Bernardo (10)
White Court School, Great Notley

My Little Penpoonpig

My penpoonpig's favourite food is Froot Loops.
Sometimes she sneaks some popcorn too, she is
very sneaky.

She lives in a woody forest, she loves it.
She can sleep there all day and night.

She loves to dance, prance and last but not least,
She loves to show off, she is a queen.

My penpoonpig goes on the stage a lot,
She is a dance queen, she stares at the mirror.

My penpoonpig is made up of a pig, cat and snake.
She is very furry and scary. She is cute and funny.

She loves to roll in muddy puddles and sleep.
She does not come out of her bed.

Poppy Chambers (10)
White Court School, Great Notley

The Magnificent Superhero Mog

Magnificent Mog is here to save the day
So come on, people, move out the way.
Even though he may be fluffy
He can sometimes be a bit scruffy.

Sometimes when he is flying
He gets hit by a pigeon without even crying.
When Mog flies he is in a disguise,
He sometimes gets bitten by flies.

Mog likes to eat fish
Which he finds very delish.

With a sniff and a snoff of his very clever nose
He carefully tiptoes all the way back to his family home.

All snuggled up in his family bed
Ready for the next day ahead.

Imogen Louise Sibley (9)
White Court School, Great Notley

My Elemental Shark

My elemental shark is super fair
Because he is half megalodon and half elemental,
He's very powerful and friendly too.

I discovered him in the deep, dark ocean
Whilst fishing with my dad
Elliott was a baby back then
He was all alone
So I decided to take him home.

He lets you play and his favourite food is plankton
He will cheer you up when you are sad.

When night falls and it is time for him to sleep
He burrows into the sand and stays there till
morning.

I love my elemental shark and you should too!

Ethan Gold (10)
White Court School, Great Notley

Dan The Dragon

D angerous like jumping off a cliff.
A ggressive like a mountain lion.
N oisy as a tiger roaring.

T owering high like the Eiffel Tower, soaring.
H armful like the world war.
E xtraordinary like finding £500 on the floor.

D eathly like a snake around your neck.
R ough like shoving yourself onto the deck.
A mazing like mighty Big Ben.
G reedy like a bear gobbling a hen.
O ptimistic like a gambler placing a bet.
N ever goes to a vet.

Oliver Reid (10)
White Court School, Great Notley

Jake The Superhero Snake

Jake the snake was near,
When you go near he will snap at you in fear
I have had him all year!

And then before I said a word,
He flew away (like a bird)
I heard he was a superhero.

I saw Jake fly,
He saved a person before they died,
I saw his green fur in the sky.

Jake had a boyfriend
Who was very proper,
His boyfriend was an otter.

Jake acts like a dog,
He jumps like a frog
And Jake sits on a log.

Jake has orange dots,
He has lots,
Jake sometimes hides in pots.

Louie Knott (10)
White Court School, Great Notley

Hippy Hoppy Harriet

Hippy Hoppy Harriet is a lazy, wild duck.
She likes to play, she likes to slide,
And most of all she likes to hide.
Harriet likes to lay all day,
Always in May every day.

Having chocolate and crisps
Without any dips makes her have a little lick.
She likes to stand and have a band
And likes to watch all the birds.
Harriet likes to dance and prance
When she goes to France.

As she lays on the bay
She celebrates her birthday.
Harriet is a shy, furry duck
And is very grumpy at all she does.

Isabel Gladen (9)
White Court School, Great Notley

Rockstar Rocky

Rockstar Rocky is sometimes shy
But when he is on stage
He tries not to cry.

He likes to play his guitar
He likes to eat brownies too
But he can be quite messy
Especially on the loo.

His incredible talent
Is known around the world
When he goes to bed
He decides to curl.

Rocky is adorable and cute
He is trying to learn the flute.

Rockstar Rocky is a hedgehog
And hates any bog.

He has a guitar which is light purple
His favourite animal is a turtle.

Amelia Coulson (10)
White Court School, Great Notley

Girelephant

G effery is my pet mixed between an elephant and a giraffe.

I t has elephant features with an elephant's nose and face.

R ising as high as a jungle tree.

E ating all the yummy green plants and leaves.

L eaving a trail of mess.

E njoying her beauty sleep from all the plants she ate.

P laying in the water, splashing everywhere.

H appily getting wet.

A nnoyingly stomping everywhere.

N ot bothering to get dry.

T ripping all the other animals.

Jemima Knighton (10)

White Court School, Great Notley

My Pet, Rosie

My pet, Rosie, is really friendly
But sometimes she is lazy.
Sometimes she is messy
So we have to keep her tidy.

She is really clever
But she can be a darer.
Rosie is easy to pet
Since she is a bright petal.

My pet, Rosie, is really marvellous
But she can get dangerous.
She is not wild
But she can be if you're not careful.

Sometimes she is crazy
As well as she is lazy.
My pet, Rosie, is as cute as a polar bear
But beware... she is there.

Dominic Baktai (10)
White Court School, Great Notley

Aquadog And Teady

My dog has chocolate fur.
He hates it when he hears a purr.

He swims through the lake
To save anyone from a quake.

In the day he is a dog,
In the night he is a hero in a bog... Aquadog!

Even a hero needs some help
When there is a yelp.

My new dog, out of the fog, Teady,
Hero of the sea,
But he hates eating a pea.

Teady has the power to turn into a bear
After chasing a hair.

So the heroes stand with pride
On the sea tide.

Lucas Simpson (10)
White Court School, Great Notley

Shocodile

I have a pet shocodile.
It is the only one in the world.
He is as big as two buses.
He is as hungry as a human.

Not everyone loves him
Because he's scary and aggressive
But inside he loves you,
You just can't see it.

He loves to eat a lot,
Especially fish.
Sometimes we give him seal
Because it is his favourite food.

I don't know why everyone hates him,
He is so lovely and happy,
I wish everyone loved my pet shocodile.

Alfie Reeve (10)
White Court School, Great Notley

Dolly The Dolphin

D olly the dolphin is a very joyful and playful pet.

O ranges are her treat food but mainly feeds on fish.

L ucky charms she loves to find around the clear blue sea.

P erfectly fun and a non-vicious dolphin, super fun to play with.

H er favourite things to do are playing and swimming around but her all-time fave is humans.

I nquisitive and has super smooth skin.

N arwhals are similar to the dolphin species but just with a horn on its head.

Khloe Williamson (10)
White Court School, Great Notley

Tales Of Polly

Let me tell you about my pet parrot,
She likes to shout.
Her name is Polly
And she likes to lick a lolly.
She has fur
And she calls herself 'her'.
She likes to walk and she likes to stalk.
She flies up to the sky,
But remembers she can't fly.
She likes to eat
But she always repeats.
Polly is a copycat
But she likes to copy Matt.
When she's mad she starts to shout,
Then she says, "Yout!" which means 'out'.

Lia Dicker (9)
White Court School, Great Notley

Always Happy

Flipping in the air,
He loves to stare.
His favourite food is cheese
And he is very pleased.

Messing up a room,
He used a wooden broom.
All about he likes to shout.
He likes wearing his super suit,
I think it's super cute.
I'm surprised it hasn't had a rip
Although he's actually very fit.

Happy has a friend called Yappy,
He carries his bone with a snappy phone.
Happy likes a seat
But now he's asleep!

Ellie-Rose Porter (10)
White Court School, Great Notley

Silly Sausage

My dog is called Silly Sausage
Who thinks he is a sizzling savoury.

When we have sizzling sausages
He has lots of powdery porridge.

He likes to walk with begging Billy
But tries to walk with lovely Lily.

When we cook on the handy hob
He comes to look by the moaning mop.

He likes to wander around the humorous house
But ends up afraid of the miniature mouse.

After this the mice meet up
While avoiding lousy lice.

Alex Levine (10)
White Court School, Great Notley

Floy The Flying Flamingo

Floy wanted to fly
But he didn't know how,
And he was a bit shy,
Up until now!

Floy wanted to fly
And he didn't want to lie,
He just wanted to cry
But all he wanted to do was fly.

Floy wanted to fly,
He wanted to sigh,
He almost gave up
But then out of the blue he flew.

If I gave up I would never have flown,
For my birthday I made a special stone,
But he won't go high
In case he would die!

Aimee Baker (10)
White Court School, Great Notley

Silly Sam

In moving slow
He sticks and sticks.
While dreaming of a big huge Twix.

He needs to hurry up
It's almost six.
While strolling along he licks his lips.

My pet has eyes as blue as the sky
But he wonders why he has five wide tentacles.

He's craving food but he's not in the mood
All he wants is to go on a cruise.

He's really tired, he needs a snooze
So he hurries up
He hasn't got time to lose.

Sophia Tillbrook (10)
White Court School, Great Notley

Livbo The Dog

Livbo the dog liked to play,
That's all she thought about every day.

Her favourite trick is to jump and get treats,
Although her favourite food is actually meat.

For her second birthday she got a new bed,
But she would rather get a red ball instead.

When she's bored she goes for a walk,
On her way she finds a fork.

When she's home she has a big sleep,
Near the fireplace every week.

Olivia Blackaby (10)
White Court School, Great Notley

Hungry Henry

Who flies, who dives,
Never eats pies,
He likes chips
But has no lips.

Mostly grumpy,
Feet are very stumpy.

Tiny but mighty,
Grandma in her nineties.

His name is Henry,
Very bendy,
He likes his chicken tendy,
Always asleep on Wednesdays.

Like a slippery snake,
Mostly awake,
People think he's fake.

This is the end,
He's a really good friend.

Taylor Johnson (9)
White Court School, Great Notley

My Pet Droner Cobra

Let me tell you about my pet king droner cobra.
He likes to dress up in a toga.
He's crossed with a big black cat
And he likes a pat.

All his snake friends have a cat
And they have a pet.
For a treat the big black cat gets some meat.
He's a cuddly lad and I'm his dad.

He scares pigs off,
They don't dare to mess with his venom.
Sometimes he's hungry, oh man!

Harry Cross (9)
White Court School, Great Notley

Person The Pug

Person the pug drunk out the mug.
Usually he drinks out of the mug
But now he eats from it.
George the pug also has a mug.

Person's favourite food is parrot
But he doesn't like juicy carrots.

He wears a mug on his head
So he can drink it at any time.

He works at a bank
Because his boat sank.
He used to be a fisherman
And now he's a banker.

Franklyn Limber (9)
White Court School, Great Notley

Larry The Vicious Lion

Larry the lion, hunting for meat
Looming in the darkness, tip-toeing on feet.

Larry the lion, growling under his breath,
Ready to pounce animals to their death.

Larry the lion's favourite thing to eat,
Is the juicy leftover meat.

Larry the lion is like a beast,
He'll make you jump in fear.
He is so big and scary
You wouldn't want to go near.

Thomas James (9)
White Court School, Great Notley

Love Mustard Bloo

My name is Mustard Bloo,
But I'm sorry I might eat your shoe.
I'm as yellow as the sun
With green stripes and blue spots.
I like jumping in some flower pots,
Don't imagine I'm that cute.
I have attitude issues,
I love my food, I get pretty rude.
My brother gurgles,
He always cries all the time.
My brother is as blue
As the Tottenham Hotspur kit.

Charlie Sellers (9)
White Court School, Great Notley

My Peculiar Pet, Rosie

Let me tell you about my pet, Rosie
Who likes to roll in bedsheets and keep cosy
But she can also be quite lazy
And is very funny.

Coming home from the walk
She likes to rest on the log.
She has a horse body
And the legs of a dog
And she likes to sniff a frog.

The more I give her she wants more
And sometimes she wants to eat the floor.

Amelia Bullus (10)
White Court School, Great Notley

The Hip Hop Goat

Jerry the hip hop goat,
Jerry who is a clever goat,
He likes eating all day,
His birthday is in May.

He likes to dance,
He likes to prance,
But most of all he likes
To go to France with all his friends.

Jerry the hip hop goat,
Jerry who is a clever goat,
He likes chocolate and crisps,
Without any dips.

Orla Martin (10)
White Court School, Great Notley

Chilled, Clever, Clawed Conrad

Clever Conrad in the sun
His fur shines gold and brown
He is proud of catching criminals in his town
Conrad is the best police dog ever!
But he needs a rest today
He's been busy and it's nearly May
And in the morning
He gets a meat treat on his seat
He is guarding the police station
And is the king of the town now.

Finn Lawford (10)
White Court School, Great Notley

Flamey The Flamingo

F lamey the flamingo always tells us what to do.

L egs as long as trees,

A lways balancing on one.

M agnificent beaks for prodding or greedily eating fish.

I ncredible shades of pink.

N ice but bossy.

G orgeous fluffy wings, as wide as a truck.

O verall Flamey is an amazing bird.

Gabriella Lane (9)

White Court School, Great Notley

Double Trouble Wobble!

With wrinkles like Grandma's
Pugs are so cute,
They spend most of their day asleep, on mute.

Burritos are a pug's favourite food,
But chicken puts them in a crazy mood.
They wobble like chickens going side to side
And love nothing more than going on a ride
And go to sleep lazily saying 'goodnight'.

Ashley Taylor (9)
White Court School, Great Notley

My Naughty Spider

My naughty spider stole my chocolate
And greedily ate all of it.

He also stole all the dog's treats
With an agile twist.

Yesterday, there were no biscuits.
I thought it was my pet spider
But it was my dog and his friend, Snider.

They were as sneaky as a mouse
In a massive brown house.

Daniel James Walker (9)
White Court School, Great Notley

My Pet, G Pellacon

G od of the pelican.

P izza is his favourite food.
E ats elephants' ears.
L oves to play football.
L ikes to rap.
A rchie is his best friend.
C oncrete is the floor of his house.
O pposite of shy.
N aughty on stage but nice off stage.

Archie Murphy (9)
White Court School, Great Notley

My Pet, Dogadile

D oes have a golden chain.
O ften plays outside in the garden.
G igantic body like a giraffe.
A very cute dogadile.
D oes live in a normal house.
I ndependent animals and works alone.
L ong tail like a kangaroo.
E ats chicken nuggets from McDonald's.

Isla Mooney (10)
White Court School, Great Notley

Reaper

R eaper is my made-up pet, named after a fire creature
E vil and naughty, throwing fireballs and garden leaves
A dventurous around the universe
P lanet to planet he roams
E nergetic, never tired of running
R eaper, I wish I could join you on a mission.

Harrison Aldred (10)
White Court School, Great Notley

Funky Frog

Funky Frog, why are you sitting on a dog?
Why don't you sit on Magnificent Mog?
Actually, why don't you sit on a log with the dog?
And Magnificent Mog hogged the log
And pushed Funky Frog and the dog off the log.
Funky Frog and the dog went to the bog and sat
on another log.

Carson Oram (10)
White Court School, Great Notley

Kolby And His Spectacular Cat

Spider Cat,
The spectacular cat.
He's a caring cat,
He's been bitten
Like a kitten.
He likes to web swing
And see what he can slay.
He's a caring cat,
He likes to eat rats
And protect the innocent.
So... he's a cat
And he's mine!

Kolby Bronze (10)

White Court School, Great Notley

Danny The Dinosaur

Danny the dinosaur was very tall
Because people told jokes around him.

And there was one thing no one knew
If he laughed his neck would grow taller.

Because of this he tried not to laugh
But the jokes just kept coming
And his laughs made him smile with glee.

Alfie Joyce (9)
White Court School, Great Notley

My Pet, Cooper

C ooper loves parrots.

O nly if it smells like carrots.

O n the grass he likes to bask.

P izza is his favourite food but only eating under the sun.

E arly in the morning he likes to yawn.

R abbits in the distance for a little treat to eat.

Harriet Snow (10)
White Court School, Great Notley

My Pet Is Snowy

S nowy is kind and helpful and mostly strong when he needs to be.

N osy but not undercover.

O nly loves carrots and grass.

W hen people come to my house they are too scared to hold him.

Y ou will often find him moving your heavy stuff for you.

Lily-Mai Bull (10)
White Court School, Great Notley

Sholphin

Swimming through the sassy sea
He swam through the slime
Like a lion sprinting through a field.
Penguins are his favourite food,
He chomps and nibbles
Which puts him in a good mood.
On his back is a large fin
Which sticks out and helps him spin.

Alfie Eley (10)
White Court School, Great Notley

My Guinea Pigs, Lazy And Hazy

My two guinea pigs with brown and grey fur
Were so hungry so they started to purr.

One hot summer day Lazy and Hazy went to play.
Throughout the day they ate some hay.

Lazy took Hazy for lunch
But all he did was munch, munch, munch.

Nevaeh Matheou (10)
White Court School, Great Notley

My Slider

S pecial pet to have.

L ittle but highly venomous.

I wouldn't go near him.

D id his favourite food (which was very nice).

E rm, he's finished and still hungry.

R un away from him so you don't die!

James Bullus (10)
White Court School, Great Notley

Snalon

S lithers like a tornado.
N aughty, nosy lion.
A pple trees are where they live.
L azy like a teenager on a weekend.
O range mane like an autumn tree.
N oisy like a car engine.

Eshaan Patel (10)
White Court School, Great Notley

Busta

B usta loves biscuits

U sually if they are beef flavoured.

S ometimes he eats the leftovers.

T he owners are very kind like Busta.

A s fast as lightning and brave like a fearsome lion.

Noah Murphy (10)
White Court School, Great Notley

Daisy The Flying Snake And Butterfly

D aisy the delicate butterfly flies through the clouds

A crobatic dancing while backflipping

I n and out of the flowers

S lowly she goes home

Y oung and happy forever.

Yhana Kuta (10)
White Court School, Great Notley

YOUNG WRITERS
INFORMATION

We hope you have enjoyed reading this book – and that you will continue to in the coming years.

If you're a young writer who enjoys reading and creative writing, or the parent of an enthusiastic poet or story writer, visit our website **www.youngwriters.co.uk/subscribe** to join the World of Young Writers and receive news, competitions, writing challenges, tips, articles and giveaways! There is lots to keep budding writers motivated to write!

If you would like to order further copies of this book, or any of our other titles, then please give us a call or order via your online account.

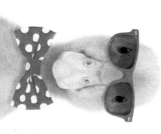

Young Writers
Remus House
Coltsfoot Drive
Peterborough
PE2 9BF
(01733) 890066
info@youngwriters.co.uk

Join in the conversation!
Tips, news, giveaways and much more!

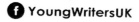 YoungWritersUK   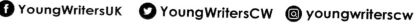 YoungWritersCW    youngwriterscw